ANNUAL 2002

SAM DENHAM

CARLTON BOOKS

THIS IS A CARLTON BOOK

PUBLISHED BY CARLTON BOOKS LIMITED 2001

20 Mortimer Street
London W1N 7RD

Text and design © 2001 Carlton Books Limited

TM and © 1967 and 2001 Carlton International Media Limited.
CAPTAIN SCARLET is a Gerry Anderson Production.
Licensed by Carlton International Media Limited.

www.captainscarlet.tv

A CIP catalogue record for this book is available from the
British Library.

ISBN 1 84222 404 2

PROJECT EDITOR: Lesley Levene
DESIGN: Claire Cooper
PRODUCTION: Garry Lewis

TO: ALL SPECTRUM PERSONNEL

FROM: COLONEL WHITE,
          COMMANDER-IN-CHIEF, SPECTRUM

Members of Spectrum...

Since the World President first invited me to form the élite global security force that we now know as Spectrum, I have worked tirelessly to build an organization that, with your help, will serve the best interests of our planet.

It has now become clear that a new danger threatens the Earth, a danger that Spectrum is fully equipped to confront.

Details of this new threat to our planet are included in this special operations manual, and it is essential that the contents which follow remain a closely guarded secret. To avoid mass panic, the people of the world must learn nothing of the strange and powerful menace we have to overcome.

I know I can rely on you. Spectrum is Green!

CONTENTS

SPECTRAFILE:
SPECTRUM IS GREEN

MAXIMUM SECURITY BUILDING, NEW YORK

PRESIDENTIAL SUITE

THE WORLD PRESIDENT

The year is 2068... After centuries of conflict, the world is almost entirely united under the control of a democratically elected World President. The few independent states that still pose a threat to world security are closely monitored and ultimate responsibility for the planet's security is now in the hands of the Spectrum organization.

Formed at the express wishes of the World President and answerable directly to him, Spectrum operates from a giant aerial platform hovering in the Earth's upper atmosphere.

From here, Spectrum's Commander-in-Chief, Colonel White, controls a team of top field agents, a flight of supersonic fighters and a network of ground support staff. Equipped with the latest technology, including hovercrafts, jet-copters and a fleet of strategically positioned armoured cars, Spectrum is ready to face any threat to world peace.

Following the detection of mysterious radio signals from an uncharted region of the planet Mars, Spectrum was immediately assigned to investigate. Commanded by top field agent Captain Black, a Zero X mission was launched, but as its Martian Excursion Vehicle approached the location of the transmissions, all contact was lost.

Only when the spaceship returned to Earth weeks later did Spectrum finally begin to learn the truth from Captain Black's crew: a terrifying race of aliens known only as the Mysterons had sworn vengeance for an unprovoked attack on their Martian city. Reported to be a changed man, Captain Black himself has not been seen since the craft touched down on its return to Earth.

Now Spectrum has a new purpose. Colonel White and his dedicated team must learn everything they can about the power of the Mysterons, so that they can counter the horrifying threats of vengeance being received from the planet Mars!

SPECTRAFILE:
CLOUDBASE COMMAND

CLOUDBASE

Length: 630 feet   **Width:** 330 feet

Power System: Solar Accelerator Panels and Atomic Turbines

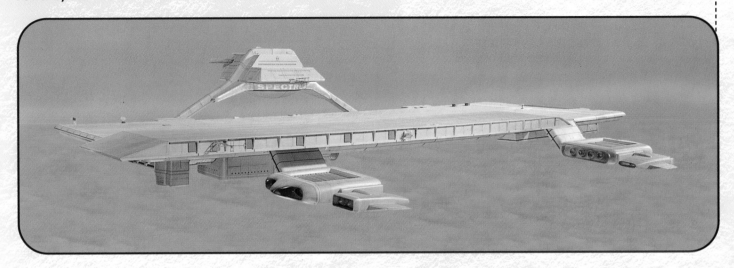

After plans to base Spectrum on a floating island, in a submarine or in outer space were rejected, the idea of constructing a giant airborne carrier was put forward – and immediately approved. Hovering at a height of 40,000 feet above the Earth, Cloudbase was constructed to provide Spectrum with an entirely self-contained mobile command centre. Home to nearly 600 Spectrum personnel, the base is equipped with a complex system of communications and monitoring equipment, controlled by a Transplast master unit in the Cloudbase Control Room. Also aboard are a fully equipped medical centre, leisure facilities, and hangars and workshops for Spectrum's Passenger Jets and the Angel Interceptors. These form Spectrum's first line of aerial attack and are piloted by a team of five female pilots, three of whom are on constant stand-by, one on the flight deck and two in the Amber Room beneath the Interceptors' launch runway.

The nerve centre of the carrier is Colonel White's desk in the Control Room. From here he can contact Spectrum agents around the world and individual field agents via their personal communication systems. Activated by colour-coded signal transceivers linked to sensory pick-ups in caps or helmets, the system allows Spectrum members to remain in constant contact. A coded system of acronyms has also been introduced to improve communication response time. "S.I.G." – short for "Spectrum is Green" – confirms a command will be carried out, or that a situation is under control. "S.I.R." – or "Spectrum is Red" – warns that an order cannot be carried out, or that danger threatens.

With Cloudbase and its communication system fully tested and operational, Spectrum is now ready to face any threat the Mysterons may pose.

CONTROL ROOM

CONFERENCE ROOM

AMBER ROOM

MISSION CODE: THE MYSTERONS

"This is the voice of the Mysterons. We know that you can hear us, Earthmen. Our first act of retaliation will be to assassinate your World President."

REPORT FILED BY:

COLONEL WHITE

"Since Spectrum first learned of the mysterious happenings on Mars from the crew of the ill-fated Zero X mission, we have been on constant alert. When the Mysterons' threat against the President was confirmed by the Zero X flight recorder, I immediately made special arrangements to ensure his total security."

FROM MY CONTROL DESK ON CLOUDBASE I PUT THROUGH A CALL TO MY FIELD AGENTS.

CAPTAIN SCARLET WAS AT THE WHEEL OF A PATROL CAR WITH CAPTAIN BROWN.

THIS IS COLONEL WHITE CALLING CAPTAIN SCARLET. PLEASE REPORT YOUR POSITION.

PROCEEDING AS PLANNED TO RENDEZVOUS WITH THE WORLD PRESIDENT AND ESCORT HIM TO NEW YORK.

CAPTAIN BROWN, I'M PUTTING YOU IN CHARGE OF THIS OPERATION.

CAPTAIN SCARLET WAS QUICK TO CONGRATULATE HIM.

S.I.G

YOUR FIRST BIG ASSIGNMENT. I WISH YOU LUCK.

BUT THE MYSTERONS DID NOT BELIEVE IN LUCK...

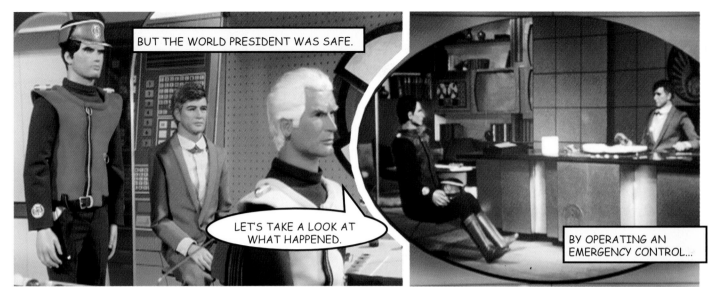

WITHIN MINUTES, CAPTAIN SCARLET WAS AIRBORNE...

WITH AN ANGEL FLIGHT ESCORT.

BUT THEN I RECEIVED SOME DISTURBING NEWS.

SPECTRUM NEW YORK REPORTS BODY OF CAPTAIN BROWN DISCOVERED NEAR SCENE OF CAR CRASH.

CAPTAIN SCARLET WAS THERE.

WHATEVER HAPPENED TO CAPTAIN BROWN MAY ALSO HAVE HAPPENED TO CAPTAIN SCARLET.

CONTACT DESTINY ANGEL IMMEDIATELY AND TELL HER TO ESCORT CAPTAIN SCARLET BACK TO CLOUDBASE.

BUT IT WAS NO USE.

CLOUDBASE, CAPTAIN SCARLET DOES NOT ANSWER.

I REALIZED THAT THE PRESIDENT WAS IN SERIOUS DANGER.

DESTINY ANGEL, MAKE A DUMMY ATTACK ON CAPTAIN SCARLET. AND MAKE SURE YOU MISS!

AS CAPTAIN SCARLET'S AIRCRAFT CROSSED THE ENGLISH COAST, DESTINY CARRIED OUT MY ORDERS.

CLOUDBASE, CAPTAIN SCARLET AND THE WORLD PRESIDENT HAVE EJECTED!

THE PLAN WORKED.

I IMMEDIATELY CONTACTED SPECTRUM HEADQUARTERS, LONDON.

HAVE THE NEAREST SPV ON THE ROAD IMMEDIATELY.

S.I.G.

MEANWHILE, DESTINY ANGEL WAS ON THE SCENE.

CAPTAIN SCARLET HAS TAKEN THE PRESIDENT TO A NEARBY CAR. THEY ARE NOW HEADING IN A NORTHERLY DIRECTION.

NOW IT WAS UP TO CAPTAIN BLUE.

PURSUIT VEHICLE A69 PLEASE.

THE UNDERCOVER AGENT OPERATED A CONTROL...

AND, WITH THE ANGELS' HELP, CAPTAIN BLUE WAS SOON IN PURSUIT OF CAPTAIN SCARLET.

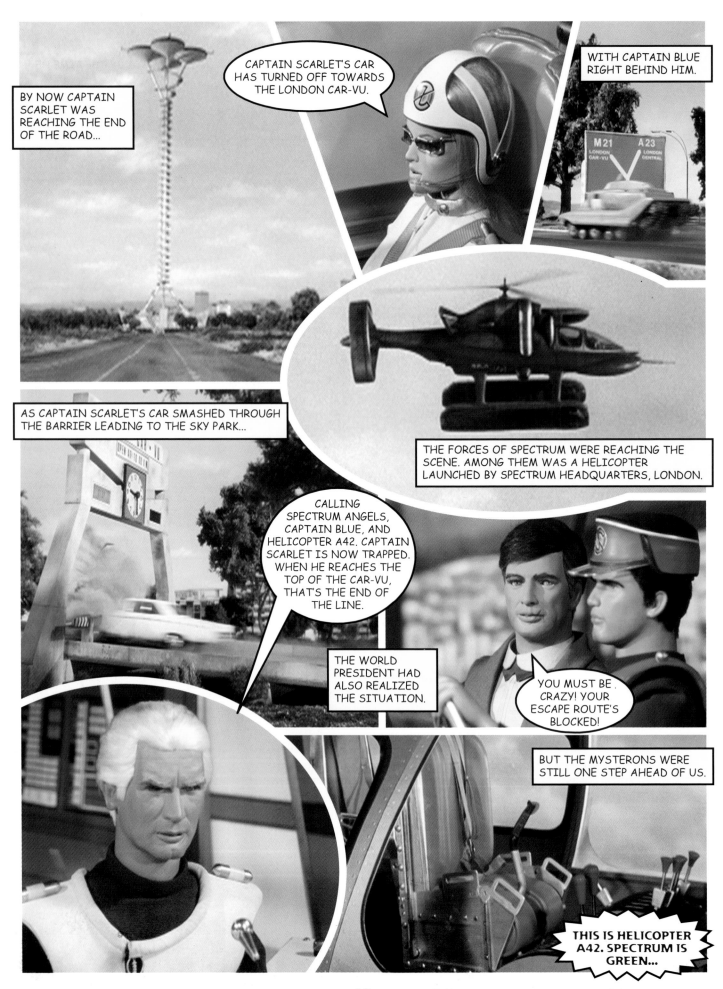

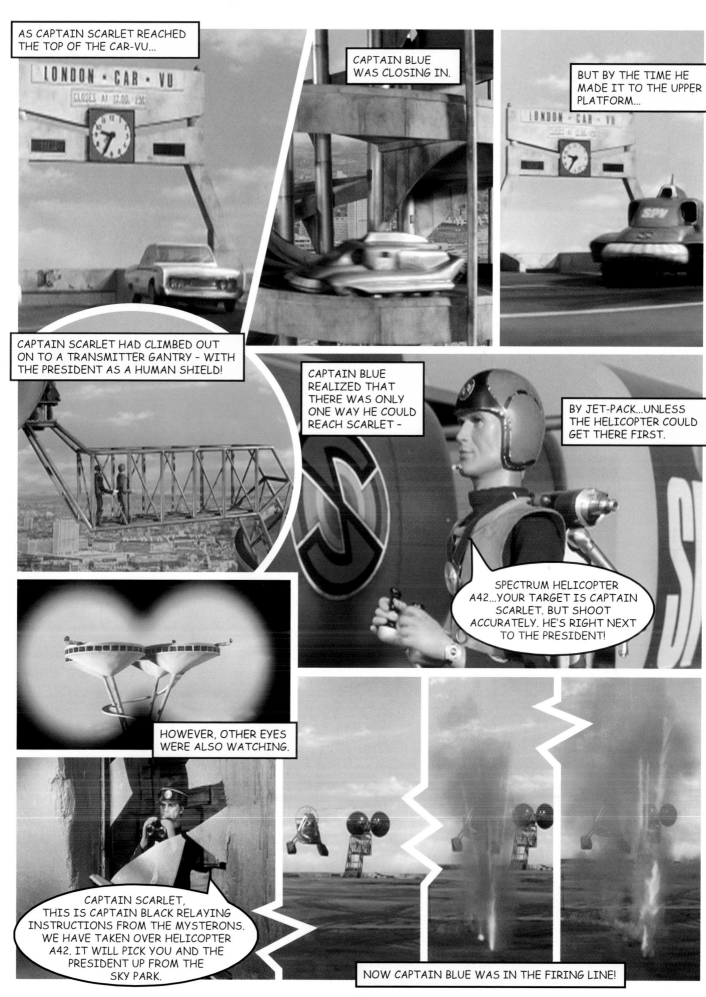

DESTINY ANGEL! HELICOPTER A42 IS FIRING AT ME! IT MUST NOW BE CONSIDERED AS HOSTILE.

WHILE CAPTAIN BLUE PLAYED CAT AND MOUSE WITH THE HELICOPTER –

DESTINY ANGEL CAME IN FOR THE ATTACK.

A MISSILE BLASTED FROM HER AIRCRAFT...

AND SCORED A DIRECT HIT!

BUT NOW THE HELICOPTER WAS ON A CRASH COURSE...

WITH THE CAR-VU!

THE COLOURS OF SPECTRUM

Spectrum's senior operatives and field commanders have been recruited from the best available personnel throughout the world. Coded by colour, they form a dedicated and efficient team.

COLONEL WHITE

Real Name:
Charles Gray

Date of Birth:
14 July 2017

Place of Birth:
London, England

Educated at King's College, Canterbury, and Norwich University. An early recruit to the World Navy, White rose rapidly to the rank of admiral before announcing his surprise resignation from active service in 2047. This was to conceal his recruitment to the Universal Secret Service. After nearly twenty years with the USS, he was then approached to command the Spectrum organization – and enthusiastically took on the new challenge.

CAPTAIN SCARLET

Real Name:
Paul Metcalfe

Date of Birth:
17 December 2036

Place of Birth:
Winchester, England

Born into a military family, Scarlet enrolled in America's prestigious West Point Military Academy after graduating from Winchester University. He then worked his way up through the World Air Force, soon reaching the rank of colonel. Spectrum's selection committee realized he was ideally qualified to join the force as their number-one agent and would not regret their decision to offer him the unique privilege.

CAPTAIN BLUE

Real Name:
Adam Svenson

Date of Birth:
26 August 2035

Place of Birth:
Boston, USA

Educated at Harvard, Blue enrolled in the World Aeronautic Society, intent on becoming a test pilot. Impressed by his energy and drive, his superiors persuaded him to help them overhaul their security department. Reluctant at first, he soon realized that the work was essential in order to prevent sensitive secrets falling into the wrong hands. His dedication to the task paid off with an invitation to join Spectrum's team of field officers, which he immediately accepted.

LIEUTENANT GREEN

Real Name:
Seymour Griffiths

Date of Birth:
18 January 2041

Place of Birth:
Port of Spain, Trinidad

A gifted musician, Green became fascinated by tele-communications at an early age. Craving excitement, he joined the World Aquanaut Security Patrol as a hydromics operative. His skills were soon recognized and he was promoted to run Marineville's new communications section. His expertise led Spectrum to make him their first choice as Colonel White's right-hand man, with special responsibilities for Spectrum's revolutionary communications system.

CAPTAIN BLACK

Real Name:
Conrad Turner

Date of Birth:
17 March 2029

Place of Birth:
Manchester, England

Orphaned in an atomic attack during the war that broke out in 2028, Captain Black was brought up by a distant relative who provided him with a good education, but no real sense of family. After joining the British Air Force, he won world recognition during the British Civil War of 2047 for heroically saving his base from a sabotaged bomber. While recovering from his wounds he revealed that his one ambition was to see world peace. Recruited to the newly formed World Space Patrol, he won further recognition. Following the announcement of Spectrum's formation, Colonel White declared that Black was exactly the kind of man the new organization needed. Without hesitation, he became Spectrum's first recruit and was the obvious choice to lead a Zero X mission to investigate the source of mysterious transmissions from Mars.

CAPTAIN MAGENTA

Real Name:
Patrick Donaghue

Date of Birth:
17 May 2034

Place of Birth:
Dublin, Ireland

Having moved to a rundown area of New York at a young age, Magenta grew up among the city's criminal gangs, but his willingness to study earned him a scholarship to Yale. Despite finding employment as a computer programmer after graduating, he soon tired of the lack of excitement and returned to crime. The offer of a free pardon and the challenge of working for Spectrum finally persuaded him to turn his back on criminal activities.

CAPTAIN GREY

Real Name:
Bradley Holden

Date of Birth:
4 March 2033

Place of Birth:
Chicago, USA

After graduating from San Diego's World Navy Academy, Grey enrolled in the submarine service, and proved his tactical brilliance many times. Joining the World Aquanaut Security Patrol, he was appointed security commander with special responsibility for the Stingray prototype. His service record and security experience impressed Spectrum's recruitment panel, who regarded him as an ideal addition to their field agent team.

DR FAWN

Real Name:
Edward Wilkie

Date of Birth:
10 July 2031

Place of Birth:
Yalumba, Australia

Having studied medicine at Brisbane University, Fawn joined the World Medical Organization as an assistant controller and soon became administrator for the advancement of medicine. Seeing the need to modernize the service, he introduced robot doctors, equipped to carry out complete diagnostic checks. When Spectrum was looking for an expert physician with administrative abilities, he was their first choice and now faces a new life on Cloudbase.

CAPTAIN OCHRE

Real Name:
Richard Fraser

Date of Birth:
23 February 2035

Place of Birth:
Detroit, USA

With little formal training and lacking the qualifications to pursue his dream of joining the World Army Air Force, Ochre enrolled in the World Government Police Corps. Assigned to one of Chicago's toughest precincts, his ingenuity and leadership led to the infiltration and eventual destruction of a dangerous crime syndicate. His crime-fighting ability added him to Spectrum's recruitment "A" list and the global challenge persuaded him to join the force.

ASSIGNMENT GREY:
OPERATION TRACK-DOWN

"We the Mysterons will unleash the terror of Project Damocles!"

FIELD COMMANDER: CAPTAIN GREY

The Mysterons have threatened to activate a Damocles neutron device being transported from Fulmer Research Base. When all contact with the transporter was lost, Spectrum immediately cordoned off the area, and then discovered that the vehicle and its driver had been Mysteronized following a fire at the transport depot. A security guard assigned to the transporter was then found unconscious in the cordoned-off zone, but recovered to report that the device had been activated. He knew the device had been left in a nearby wood, but couldn't remember the exact location. Can you study his report carefully to see if the information he can remember contains enough clues to locate the device before it devastates the surrounding area.

SECURITY GUARD'S REPORT

When we left the research base we turned right on to the main road, then immediately left and left again. After passing between two woods, we went straight on at the next junction and crossed a railway line. Soon afterwards we turned right and crossed a river, with woods to our left.

We then turned left and drove alongside the river before taking the second left turn. We crossed the river twice, and then the railway line, before arriving at a crossroads, where we turned left again. We then turned right twice and parked in the nearest wood.

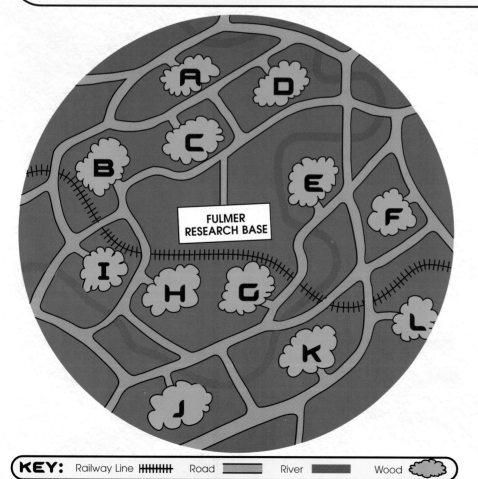

KEY: Railway Line ▮▮▮▮▮▮   Road ▭▭▭   River ▬▬▬   Wood ☁

See page 60 for Solutions

ASSIGNMENT OCHRE:
THE DEADLY HEROES

**"We the Mysterons will turn the world's heroes against their President.
We will be avenged!"**

FIELD COMMANDER: CAPTAIN OCHRE

The new Mysteron threat suggests that one or more of the winners of the Global Heroism Award are now Mysteron agents and will attempt to assassinate the President at the award ceremony. We're certain the Mysteron agents are not perfect doubles, but can you tell from the pictures taken before and after the Mysteron threat was received how many of the prize-winners are now Mysteron agents?

THE PRIZE-WINNERS BEFORE THE MYSTERON THREAT...

THE PRIZE-WINNERS AFTER THE MYSTERON THREAT!

See page 60 for Solutions

MISSION CODE: LUNARVILLE 7

"This is the voice of the Mysterons. We know that you can hear us, Earthmen. We have no quarrel with the Moon and we accept their offer of friendship. But we will continue to take our revenge against the Earth. We will be avenged!"

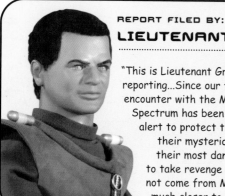

REPORT FILED BY:

LIEUTENANT GREEN

"This is Lieutenant Green reporting...Since our first terrifying encounter with the Mysterons, Spectrum has been on constant alert to protect the Earth from their mysterious power. But their most dangerous attempt to take revenge on Earth did not come from Mars, but from much closer to home..."

OVER THE LAST CENTURY, A NETWORK OF COLONIES HAS BEEN BUILT UP ON THE MOON'S SURFACE. THE MOST RECENT – LUNARVILLE 7.

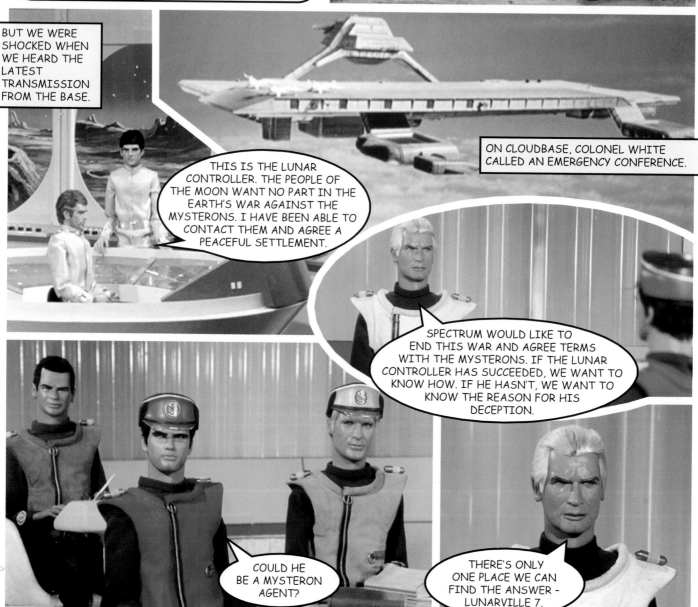

BUT WE WERE SHOCKED WHEN WE HEARD THE LATEST TRANSMISSION FROM THE BASE.

THIS IS THE LUNAR CONTROLLER. THE PEOPLE OF THE MOON WANT NO PART IN THE EARTH'S WAR AGAINST THE MYSTERONS. I HAVE BEEN ABLE TO CONTACT THEM AND AGREE A PEACEFUL SETTLEMENT.

ON CLOUDBASE, COLONEL WHITE CALLED AN EMERGENCY CONFERENCE.

SPECTRUM WOULD LIKE TO END THIS WAR AND AGREE TERMS WITH THE MYSTERONS. IF THE LUNAR CONTROLLER HAS SUCCEEDED, WE WANT TO KNOW HOW. IF HE HASN'T, WE WANT TO KNOW THE REASON FOR HIS DECEPTION.

COULD HE BE A MYSTERON AGENT?

THERE'S ONLY ONE PLACE WE CAN FIND THE ANSWER – LUNARVILLE 7.

21

22

23

AS SID EXPLODED IN CLOUDS OF SMOKE AND DEBRIS...

A CHAIN REACTION WAS SET OFF ACROSS LUNARVILLE 7.

OUR LUNAR ROCKET WAS STILL ON THE LAUNCH PAD...

AND CAPTAIN SCARLET BARELY HAD TIME TO GIVE ME THE ORDER TO LAUNCH...

TAKE OFF!

BEFORE THE ENTIRE BASE ERUPTED BENEATH US!

BACK AT CLOUDBASE, COLONEL WHITE HAD A SPECIAL MESSAGE FOR US.

WE SHALL NEVER KNOW HOW THE LUNAR CONTROLLER WAS TAKEN OVER BY THE MYSTERONS, BUT THE WORLD PRESIDENT HAS PERSONALLY ASKED ME TO THANK YOU FOR PREVENTING THEIR PLAN TO USE HIM TO TAKE CONTROL OF THE MOON.

WE HAD WON THIS BATTLE, BUT THE WAR OF NERVES WAS FAR FROM OVER...

SPECTRAFILE:
THE WINGS OF SPECTRUM

The latest aviation technology provides Spectrum with the best available combat and transport aircraft.

THE ANGEL INTERCEPTOR

Length: 60 feet   **Wingspan:** 35 feet
Weight: 40,100 lb   **Speed:** 3,000 m.p.h.

Developed from International Engineering's World Army Air Force Viper Jet, the Angel Interceptor is Spectrum's long-range single-seater fighter. Clamped to the Cloudbase catapult launch system for immediate take-off, the craft is accessed via a telescopic pressurized injector tube. On return to Cloudbase, the Interceptor lands with the aid of a hydraulic landing pad. Powered by a rear-mounted ram jet served by twin turbo-jet compressors, the aircraft is armed with a central multi-purpose cannon and side-mounted air-to-air and air-to-ground missiles.

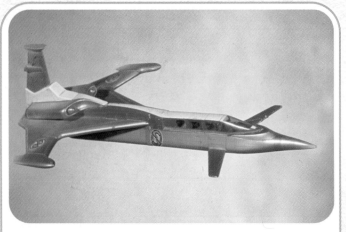

SPECTRUM PASSENGER JET (SPJ)

Length: 78 feet   **Wingspan:** 37 feet
Weight: 630,427 lb   **Speed:** 1,125 m.p.h.

Adapted from Universal Aero's prototype TVR 24 aircraft, the nine-seater passenger jet is used to transport Spectrum agents to and from Cloudbase. The passenger cabin can be adapted to a variety of functions and a revolutionary tilt-wing air-brake system enables the craft to land on short runways. Power is supplied by twin reheat turbo jets. Although not intended to be a combat aircraft, plans are being considered to fit the SPJ with a standard Angel multi-purpose cannon unit and to extend its range and speed.

SPECTRUM HELICOPTER

Length: 45 feet   **Wingspan:** 39 feet
Weight: 36,000 lb   **Speed:** 302 m.p.h.

Developed from Universal Engineering's 2066 model "Rotar" helijet, the helicopter combines helicopter and helijet technology to create a versatile high-altitude patrol vehicle. Powered by twin Mark 2 Windenown 7 air-feed turbos, the craft's unique ring-shape tailplane provides great stability and allows it to glide for some distance in the event of an engine stall. Armed with a high-explosive rocket cannon, the helicopter can carry up to five people. New modifications should increase its maximum speed to 400 m.p.h.

SPECTRAFILE:
FLIGHT OF ANGELS

Spectrum's team of fighter pilots have been selected to prove that women have an important role to play in the organization. Apart from Destiny, all have been given musical codenames.

SYMPHONY

Real Name: Karen Wainwright

Date of Birth: 6 January 2042

Place of Birth: Cedar Rapids, USA

Graduating with seven degrees, Symphony was offered a place on the Universal Secret Service training course. Qualifying in two years, she soon became the service's number-one agent. While training to fly for a special mission, she fell in love with the experience and decided to leave the USS to become a professional pilot. When Spectrum asked her to join the Angels, she realized she could combine her USS experience and love of flying in one job and proved her enthusiasm by passing the complex entrance exam in two short hours.

HARMONY

Real Name: Chan Kwan
Date of Birth: 19 June 2042
Place of Birth: Tokyo, Japan

Daughter of a flying-taxi operator, Harmony knew that flying was the only career she desired and while studying at Tokyo University she spent every spare moment at the local flying club. During an attempt to fly single-handed around the world, she received an SOS call from three men trapped on a blazing tanker. Effecting an amazing rescue, she was hailed as a heroine. An obvious candidate to join Spectrum, she is now devoted to the force and is regarded as their best pilot.

MELODY

Real Name: Magnolia Jones
Date of Birth: 10 January 2043
Place of Birth: Atlanta, USA

Sharing her older brothers' interest in fast cars, Melody left school to take up professional motor-racing and soon became an expert driver. Sent to a Swiss finishing school, she discovered she could learn to fly, and after being expelled for unruly behaviour she joined the World Army Air Force to become their most brilliant test pilot. Her amazing courage and nerves of steel led Spectrum to approach her and she readily agreed to join the new force.

DESTINY

Real Name: Juliette Pontoin
Date of Birth: 23 August 2040
Place of Birth: Paris, France

After studying at Rome University, Destiny's adventurous spirit led her to join the World Army Air Force, where she was drawn to the intelligence corps. Becoming a skilled pilot and brilliant agent, she was soon promoted to command the newly created women's fighter squadron. Impressed by her intelligence, experience and faultless WAAF record, Spectrum invited her to join their new Angel squadron and she was thrilled to accept.

RHAPSODY

Real Name: Dianne Simms
Date of Birth: 27 April 2043
Place of Birth: London, England

A law and sociology graduate of the University of London, Rhapsody became caught up in the city's swinging party scene. The life soon began to bore her, but after meeting Lady Penelope Creighton-Ward she joined the Federal Agents Bureau. Before long she was given command of the bureau and this led many other organizations to approach her. The most exciting challenge was offered by Spectrum and, after special air training, she joined the Angel team.

ASSIGNMENT MAGENTA:
THE ELECTRONIC VIRUS

"We the Mysterons will disrupt the Cloudbase computer system!"

FIELD COMMANDER: CAPTAIN MAGENTA

A Mysteron agent has introduced a programming virus into the Cloudbase computer. Your mission is to unscramble the data listed below from the memory bank and, using the remaining letters, find the name of the Mysteron responsible for planting the virus. The data could be stored in any direction, in forward or reverse order.

S.I.G.
SPECTRUM
BROWN
MELODY
MAGENTA
OCHRE
SCARLET
WHITE
BLUE
DESTINY
S.I.R.
GREY
FAWN
GREEN
SYMPHONY
HARMONY
RHAPSODY

ALIEN
MARS
SPACE
NEPTUNE
MOON
EARTHMAN
INDESTRUCTIBLE
MYSTERONS
ZERO X
EYE

PRISM
S.E.T.
SHADE
COMPLEX
PULSATOR
SPV
MACHINE
ROM
PHASE
ANGEL
CAPTAIN
CLOUDBASE
PRESIDENT

SPY
FUSE
UNIT
NET
AREA
COMPUTE
BUG
CRASH
SCANNER

```
S H A D E S P E C T R U M N
C C A C Y C O M P L E X W L
R O A R E A R H A R M O N Y
A P M N C R S P H R R O D
S T U P N L N C T B S E O O
H Y N L U E O F L A T Z M L
I N D E S T R U C T I B L E
N O K A D A E S D B N N N M
E H H W H I T E P B U W A A
E P R H A P S O D Y A G N C
R M G V L T Y E R F E S G H
G Y P R I S M O R N E T E I
I S B N E E N U T P E N L N
S C Y T N Y N A M H T R A E
```

See page 60 for Solutions

ASSIGNMENT FAWN:
THE CODED TARGET

"We the Mysterons will destroy our next target with its own name. We will be avenged!"

FIELD COMMANDER: DR FAWN

Spectrum believes that the Mysterons' latest threat is connected with the theft of four explosive-compound formulas. We're certain that one of these compounds will be used to destroy one of four high-profile targets, and that a clue to the intended target is contained within the compound formulas.

Can you rearrange the chemical abbreviations in each of the four compound formulas to find the Mysterons' target?

LUNARVILLE ONE

BEREZNIK PLANE

COMPOUND ONE
Lithium + Neon + Phosphorus + Radium + Radon + Rhenium + Silicon + Titanium

----

COMPOUND TWO
Berylium + Iodine + Lanthanum + Neon + Potassium + Rhenium + Zinc

----

COMPOUND THREE
Astatine + Barium + Calcium + Lanthanum + Nitrogen + Selenium + Titanium

----

COMPOUND FOUR
Iodine + Lithium + Neon + Nickel + Oxygen + Sodium + Vanadium

COMPOUND	ABBREVIATION
Astatine	At
Barium	Ba
Berylium	Be
Calcium	Ca
Iodine	I
Lanthanum	La
Lithium	Li
Neon	Ne
Nickel	Ni
Nitrogen	N
Oxygen	O
Phosphorus	P
Potassium	K
Radium	Ra
Radon	Rn
Rhenium	Re
Selenium	Se
Silicon	Si
Sodium	Na
Titanium	Ti
Vanadium	V
Zinc	Zn

PRESIDENT LINER

ATLANTICA BASE

See page 60 for Solutions

MISSION CODE: CRATER 101

"This is the voice of the Mysterons. We know that you can hear us, Earthmen.
Although you have discovered our complex on the Moon, it will never reveal its secrets.
Anyone who dares to enter will be destroyed!"

REPORT FILED BY:
CAPTAIN BLUE

"This is Captain Blue reporting... Within days of our last minute-escape from Lunarville 7, Captain Scarlet and I were called to a special briefing on Cloudbase. The recordings we'd made on our visit to the dark side of the Moon confirmed that the Earth was facing a new threat from the Mysterons..."

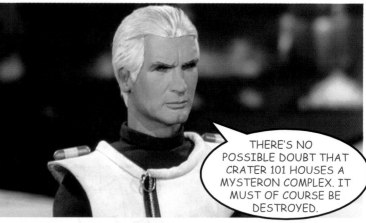

THERE'S NO POSSIBLE DOUBT THAT CRATER 101 HOUSES A MYSTERON COMPLEX. IT MUST OF COURSE BE DESTROYED.

BUT IF WE TRY TO DESTROY THE COMPLEX, THE MYSTERONS WILL USE THEIR POWERS TO RECONSTRUCT IT.

SO THIS OPERATION WILL BE DIVIDED INTO TWO ASSIGNMENTS. THE SECOND IS TO DESTROY THE COMPLEX...

AND THE FIRST?

TO SEND A VOLUNTEER FORCE INTO CRATER 101. OBJECTIVE: TO FIND AND REMOVE THE MYSTERON POWER SOURCE.

THE COLONEL DIDN'T HAVE TO LOOK ANY FURTHER FOR HIS VOLUNTEERS. SOON CAPTAIN SCARLET, LIEUTENANT GREEN AND MYSELF WERE ON A ROCKET HEADING BACK TO THE MOON.

UNAWARE OF THE NEW DANGER THAT WAS HEADING TOWARDS US, WE REACHED CRATER 101 ON SCHEDULE AND UNLOADED THE ARMOURED MOON TRACTOR.

IN FRONT OF US WERE THE MYSTERON COMPLEX...

AND THE CONTROL VEHICLE.

THE MYSTERON CRAFT CAME STRAIGHT FOR US.

WE'VE BEEN SPOTTED!

THEY'RE GOING TO ATTACK!

LIEUTENANT GREEN, MAN THE MISSILE GUN!

WITHIN SECONDS, THE CONTROL VEHICLE WAS IN HIS SIGHTS...

FIRE!

LIEUTENANT GREEN WAS DEAD ON TARGET.

WE'D KNOCKED OUT THE MYSTERON CRAFT, BUT THE DANGER WAS FAR FROM OVER.

THE MYSTERON COMPLEX WAS UNLIKE ANYTHING WE'D EVER SEEN...

A KALEIDOSCOPE OF UNEARTHLY LIGHT AND COLOUR.

IT'S INDESCRIBABLE!

THERE'S NO RADIATION...NO X-RAY OR INFRA-RED EMISSIONS...

BACK AT LUNARVILLE 6, COMMANDER NOLAN NOW REALIZED THAT WE HAD WALKED INTO A TRAP.

FRAZER IS A MYSTERON. HE'S SET THE DETONATOR FOR 10 O'CLOCK, AND CAPTAIN SCARLET'S OUT OF RADIO RANGE.

A ROCKET'S THE ONLY THING FAST ENOUGH TO REACH THEM IN TIME.

AN UNMANNED ROCKET? COULD IT WORK?

STILL UNAWARE OF THE DANGER, WE CONTINUED TO EXPLORE, UNTIL...

I THINK I'VE FOUND THE HEART OF THE COMPLEX!

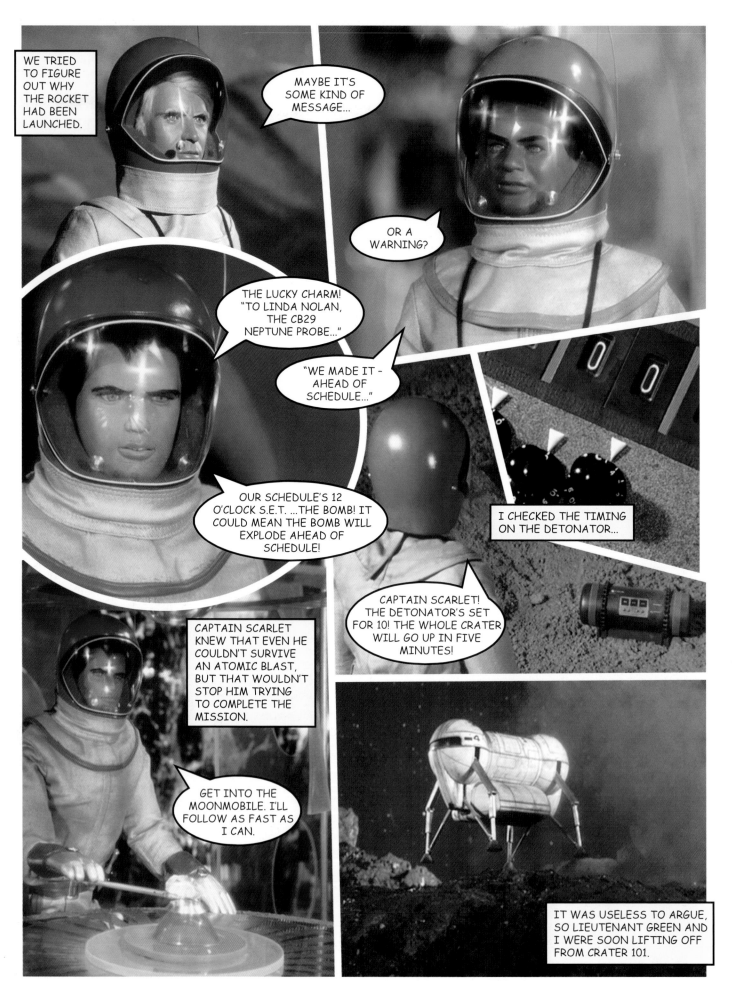

43

SPECTRAFILE:
GROUND DEFENCE

A number of different specialized vehicles are available for Spectrum's use in land-based assignments, fulfilling a range of functions.

SPECTRUM PURSUIT VEHICLE (SPV)

Length: 25 feet
Speed: 200+ m.p.h.
Weight: 8 tons

Spectrum's high-speed amphibious armoured car is propelled by a removable fuel-cell energy pack. Each of the six primary drive wheels is fitted with an individual motor and magnetic brakes. The forward set of secondary wheels is linked to the forward primary wheels to create a dual steering system. This gives the SPV exceptional road-holding ability at high speed.

Among the vehicle's unique features, the most notable is the driving position. The SPV's twin-control seats are rear-facing for greater crash safety and the vehicle is controlled via TV monitors. Seats slide outwards and are lowered to the ground by hydraulics for easy access. In the event of an emergency the seats can also be ejected by high-powered rockets and are equipped with parachutes for safe landing.

Other special features include a high-impact-resistant nose buffer, rear-mounted subsidiary tracks providing extra grip over rough terrain, a high-powered cannon and smoke screens. Specialized accessories stored in central lockers can also be powered by the SPV's energy pack. One of the most useful pieces of equipment is the one-man jet-pack, which gives agents extra field mobility.

SPECTRUM SALOON CAR (SSC)

Length: 18 feet
Top Speed: 200 m.p.h.
Weight: 29 cwt

A high-speed five-seater patrol car, the SSC is Spectrum's most widely used vehicle. Constructed of lightweight fleetonium alloy and powered by extra-boost compressed-gas turbines, its special features include a reinforced central nose ram and magnetic field brakes.

Built around a contoured ribcage, the SSC has a range of other safety features, including World Motor Manufacturers Ltd standard airbags, bullet-proof tyres and windscreens, and a high-speed stabilizing fin.

MAXIMUM SECURITY VEHICLE (MSV)

Designed to transport VIPs in utmost safety, the MSV is fitted with every conceivable survival feature. Constructed of a quadropack skin with anti-radiation layer, a prototype is rumoured to have withstood a week's trial on the World Army Air Force firing range. Solar collector strips in the central rib provide additional power to a stand-by motor connected to the vehicle's main diesel unit. Modifications to increase the MSV's speed are currently being developed.

THE YELLOW FOX SECURITY TANKER

Converted from a standard Universal Motor Co. fuel tanker, the Yellow Fox is Spectrum's covert VIP transporter and mobile conference unit. Inside its armoured tank section, Spectrum has installed a six-seater air-conditioned meeting chamber accessed by a rear-mounted hatchway. A direct video satellite link to Cloudbase allows vital meetings to be held in comfort and at speed. Yellow Fox units are stationed at major airports and Delta refineries around the world.

SPECTRUM HOVERCRAFT

A four-man atomic-powered vehicle, the 62-foot-long hovercraft can travel at speeds in excess of 100 miles per hour and is ideal for use in marshy or desert terrain. A centrally mounted revolving rotor powered by a neutron generator provides lift, while a thermionic converter supplies electric current to a compressed turbine providing forward thrust. Base Koala in Australia offers hovercraft training facilities for all Spectrum cadets.

RADAR VAN

Several fleets of radar detector vans based on a standard World Army Air Force vehicle are maintained by Spectrum to provide a ground-based search facility, or additional security coverage against air attack. Optimum monitor cabin space is achieved with the forward-mounted dual fuel-cell-powered engines. A multi-wavelength antenna ensures maximum information reception over the widest possible area.

SPECTRAFILE:
REQUISITION STATIONS

Spectrum Pursuit Vehicles are stationed around the world in concealed locations ready for immediate action. To requisition an SPV, field commanders need only show their identity pass to the undercover agent responsible for maintaining the vehicle and it is made available within seconds. A variety of worldwide SPV agent locations follow.

SPV: 021

Location:
Workshop
New York City Airport
USA

SPV: A69

Location:
Swift Removal Van
Delta Filling Station
London, England

SPV: A75

Location:
Auld Lang Syne
Whisky Plant
Glen Garry
Scotland

SPV: 104

Location:
Underground Bunker
Delta Filling Station
Arizona, USA

SPV: 428

Location:
Village Emporium
Sahara
North Africa

SPV: 503

Location:
Log Cabin
Frost Line Defence Area
Canada

SPV: 1034

Location:
Dummy Storage Tank
Delta Refinery
Bensheba District

SPV: CLASSIFIED

Location:
Casino
Monte Carlo
Monaco

SPV: CLASSIFIED

Location:
Delta Filling Station
Stone Point Village
England

MISSION CODE: DANGEROUS RENDEZVOUS

"This is the voice of the Mysterons. We know that you can hear us, Earthmen.
Our next act of retaliation will be to destroy Cloudbase.
Do you hear? Spectrum's headquarters, Cloudbase, will be destroyed at midnight!"

REPORT FILED BY:
CAPTAIN SCARLET

"On our return from the Moon with the crystal pulsator, one of the world's leading space scientists began working round the clock to learn its secrets. Finally, it seemed he'd made a breakthrough."

I WAS SENT TO THE NASH INSTITUTE OF TECHNOLOGY TO ESCORT HIM TO CLOUDBASE.

CAPTAIN SCARLET HAS ARRIVED, DR KURNITZ.

I CALLED CAPTAIN OCHRE IN THE YELLOW FOX...

AND CONFIRMED THAT WE WERE READY FOR HIM TO PICK US UP.

SPECTRUM IS GREEN.

WE WERE SOON ON OUR WAY TO THE AIRPORT.

MEANWHILE, INSIDE THE SPECIALLY CONVERTED TANKER'S SECURITY CABIN, DR KURNITZ REVEALED SOME IMPORTANT NEWS.

I KNOW THE DANGER YOU WENT THROUGH TO GET THE PULSATOR, BUT I CAN TELL YOU IT WAS WORTH IT.

BECAUSE OF YOUR EFFORTS, I BELIEVE WE WILL BE ABLE TO COMMUNICATE WITH THE MYSTERONS. LET'S HOPE THEY WILL LISTEN TO REASON.

FOLLOWING THE LATEST MYSTERON THREAT, COLONEL WHITE HAD PUT CLOUDBASE ON MAXIMUM SECURITY ALERT.

ANY PLANE, ROCKET OR SATELLITE APPROACHING THE BASE WILL BE ATTACKED.

THE ONLY EXCEPTION WILL BE THE AIRCRAFT BRINGING CAPTAIN SCARLET AND DR KURNITZ TO CLOUDBASE.

SPECTRUM HAS DONE A GOOD JOB ON THE TRANSMISSION CIRCUITS, COLONEL.

DR KURNITZ PRODUCED THE PULSATOR. WITH HIS PERMISSION...

I CAREFULLY PLACED IT IN POSITION.

IT'S PULSATING THE SAME WAY IT DID ON THE MOON!

YES, CAPTAIN. AND ONCE I'VE CHECKED THE SECONDARY CIRCUITS...

WE WILL BE ABLE TO SPEAK DIRECTLY TO THE MYSTERONS!

49

50

THEIR AIM WAS PERFECT...

AND THE RESULTS DEVASTATING!

THEN, FOR THE FIRST TIME, MEN FROM EARTH WITNESSED YOUR AMAZING POWERS OF RETRO-METABOLISM...

AND HEARD THE MYSERONS UTTER THEIR FIRST THREATS, WHICH FOR ONE OF THEM WOULD SPELL DOOM...

EARTHMEN, THIS IS THE VOICE OF THE MYSTERONS. YOU AND YOUR PEOPLE WILL PAY FOR THIS ACT OF AGGRESSION. ONE OF YOU WILL BE UNDER OUR CONTROL AND WILL BE INSTRUMENTAL IN AVENGING THE MYSTERONS.

WE ADMIT THAT THE ATTACK ON YOUR COMPLEX WAS WRONG. BUT IT WAS DONE OUT OF FEAR. ON BEHALF OF THE PEOPLES OF THE EARTH, I OFFER YOU THE HAND OF FRIENDSHIP AND HOPE IT WILL BE ACCEPTED.

ALL WE COULD DO NOW WAS WAIT... UNTIL FINALLY, A SIGNAL CAME THROUGH...

THIS IS THE VOICE OF THE MYSTERONS. IT HAS BEEN DECIDED TO ALLOW ONE MEMBER OF SPECTRUM TO MEET OUR REPRESENTATIVE. THE MEMBER OF SPECTRUM MUST NOT CARRY WEAPONS OR COMMUNICATION EQUIPMENT. FURTHER INSTRUCTIONS WILL FOLLOW.

I'LL LEAVE IMMEDIATELY.

THERE WAS NO QUESTION ABOUT WHO TO SEND ON THE MISSION.

52

53

55

SPECTRAFILE:
MYSTERON ALERT!

Since the Mysterons first declared war on Earth, Spectrum has dealt with countless threats to world security. Eyewitness statements indicate that they may share one common factor.

FROM: COLONEL WHITE

TO: ALL SPECTRUM AGENTS

From the moment Zero X touched down on Earth, following its disastrous mission to Mars, one question has remained unanswered: where is Captain Black? Reports from his fellow crew members suggest that after they witnessed the incredible reconstruction of the Mysterons' Martian complex, Black became a changed man.

Gaunt, aloof and behaving almost like an automaton, he kept himself confined to quarters throughout the long voyage home. The once fearless fighter for peace seemed a changed man, a shadow of his former self, his voice a lifeless monotone. As his co-pilot observed, "It was almost as if he had died."

Then when the craft finally landed at Glenn Field, he vanished. Now it seems there is some kind of explanation. Captain Black appears to have become the Mysterons' agent on Earth. Sightings of a mysterious pale-looking man at the scene of Mysteron attacks in locations around the world would seem to confirm this. On a number of occasions he has even been encountered by fellow members of Spectrum.

Examples of a number of these cases follow.

LOCATION: CULVER ATOMIC CENTRE, ENGLAND

Following a break-in at the centre, CCTV cameras caught Captain Black on film, confirming at last that he had returned to Earth. In the course of his escape from the centre, he was exposed to a radioactive isotope and became traceable by Geiger detector. In an attempt to capture Captain Black a trap was set, but by a twist of fate Symphony Angel became an unwitting decoy and Black escaped, but not before revealing that he had kept some of his human characteristics.

LOCATION: ARIZONA, USA

Working undercover, following a report received from Spectrum Intelligence, Captain Scarlet set himself up as a willing accomplice in a plot to destroy the subcontinent of North America.

Hoping to identify the mastermind behind the Mysteron plot, he allowed himself to be taken to a remote ranch house, where he was certain he heard the barely recognizable voice of Captain Black giving orders.

LOCATION: NEW YORK CITY, USA

When the Mysterons threatened to destroy the heart of New York, a full-scale security operation was put into action to protect the city. Investigating reports of Mysteron activity in the financial district, Captain Scarlet thought he recognized the driver of a car leaving the area.

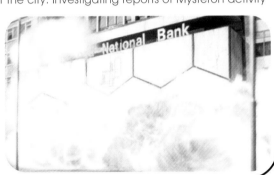

Convinced it was Captain Black, he and Captain Blue pursued the vehicle into a dead-end street, but then the car and the driver both vanished into thin air, just as the Mysterons carried out their threat.

LOCATION: EXPO 2068 SITE, CANADA

Reports that the Mysterons had hijacked a nuclear reactor bound for the Manicougan Dam project led Spectrum to mount a full-scale search to locate the device before it was activated. The reactor transport truck was soon found, but the device had been loaded on to a remote-controlled heli-freighter operated from the Expo 2068 site.

The heli-freighter controller was later discovered suffering from burns and gunshot wounds, but recovered to identify his assailant as Captain Black.

These four reports appear to prove conclusively that Captain Black is indeed working for the Mysterons – a helpless instrument in their war of nerves against the Earth. All Spectrum agents must now maintain a constant watch for this once loyal and trusted colleague, in the hope that he may one day be released from the Mysterons' control.

S.I.G.

COLONEL WHITE

ASSIGNMENT SOLUTIONS

GREY

The transporter drove along the white dotted line to Wood "F".

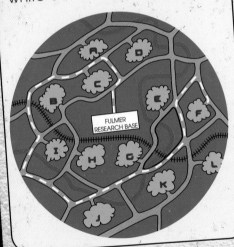

OCHRE

The red circles indicate where you will find the differences.

MAGENTA

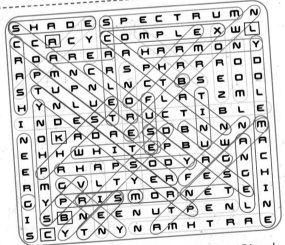

The Mysteron agent's name is Black.

FAWN

Compound Three will be used to destroy Atlantica Base.

(At + Ba + Ca + La + N + Se + Ti)